The Characters of
Christmas

by Ruth Hearson

10

A very long time ago,
God's messengers, the

ProPHetS,

told everyone that one day,
Jesus would be born.
They knew exactly where it would
happen and all about His family.
Isn't that amazing?!

An angel spoke to **Joseph** in a dream and told *him* not to be scared. It was all part of God's big plan for Mary to have a baby. The angel told Joseph to marry Mary. The angel also said they should name the baby "Jesus" because He will save His people from their sins. Hooray!

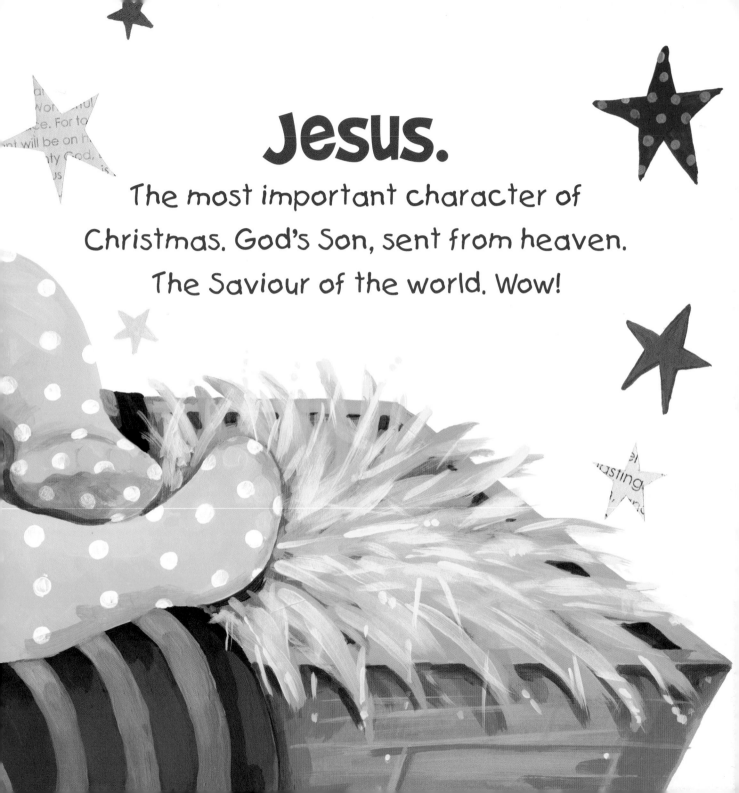

Jesus.

The most important character of Christmas. God's Son, sent from heaven. The Saviour of the world. Wow!

In the stable, **Mary**
wrapped baby Jesus in blankets
and placed Him in a manger.
Bethlehem was so busy and so full
of people, there had been no room
for them to stay anywhere else.
Oh dear!

The sky over Bethlehem
was filled with angels.
"Good news!" said one

angel,

"The Messiah has been born
today. He is Christ the Lord".
Can you imagine that?!

When the **SHEPHERDS**
had seen baby Jesus, they were so
excited they told everyone about Him.
Everything was just as the angel had
said, so the shepherds said lots of thank
you prayers to God. How lovely!

When **King Herod**
heard about Jesus,
he was not happy at all!
He hated God and didn't want
His Son Jesus to be King. Boo!

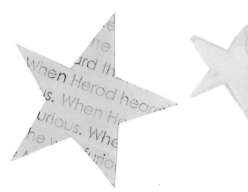

Wise men followed the
shiniest star in the sky and it took
them all the way to Bethlehem.
There, they saw Jesus and gave
Him gifts of special treasure.
It must have been like a birthday party!

The characters of Christmas
are all part of God's big story.

When **you** love and follow Jesus,
you can be part of the story too.

The Bible says that God loves
everyone in the world so much that He
sent His Son and when we choose to
be His friends, it's the beginning of the
most amazing adventure story, a story
that lasts forever! Isn't that fantastic!

(You can read the whole story and discover more about the
characters of Christmas in Matthew 1–2 and Luke 1–2.)

For all the kids at Swan Bank Church

RH